HECTOR BERLIOZ

LE CARNAVAL ROMAIN

THE ROMAN CARNIVAL
DER RÖMISCHE KARNEVAL

Overture for Orchestra

T0080496

Ernst Eulenburg Ltd

London · Mainz · Madrid · New York · Paris · Prague · Tokyo · Toronto · Zürich

HECTOR BERLIOZ
Overture: *Roman Carnival*, Op. 9

Though *Benvenuto Cellini* was derisively received on its première at the Paris Opéra on 10 September 1838, Berlioz never lost his affection for it. A little over five years later he decided to salvage at least some of what seemed to be a work that had sunk without trace, and out of two themes in the opera he fashioned a new concert *ouverture caractéristique pour grand orchestre*, naming it from the second of them *Carnaval Romain*. The overture was dedicated to Prince Friedrich von Hohenzollern-Hechingen, an enlightened patron of Berlioz's music with whom the composer had stayed during a German tour in 1842–3; Berlioz arranged various concerts of his music for the Prince's small but excellent orchestra, and after the last of them in April was awarded the Hohenzollern Cross. The first performance of the overture was conducted by Berlioz at the Salle Herz in Paris on 3 February 1844. During rehearsals for the production of the opera, he had fallen out with the conductor, F.-A. Habeneck, who was unable to achieve the fast tempo demanded by Berlioz for the saltarello in the Carnival scene. Hearing that Berlioz had been deprived of his wind players by reason of National Guard duties for the morning rehearsal of the overture's first performance, Habeneck came to the concert to watch how Berlioz himself would survive the ordeal, no doubt expecting a satisfactory disaster. 'One sees his point', observes Berlioz in his *Memoirs*:[1]

> Indeed, when I arrived in the orchestra, all the wind players crowded round me, appalled at the thought of giving a public performance of an overture that was completely unknown to them.
> 'Don't worry,' I said. 'The parts are correct, and you are all excellent players. Watch my stick as often as you can, count your rests carefully, and everything will be all right.'
> Not a single mistake occurred. I started the allegro at the right tempo, the whirlwind tempo of the Roman dancers. The audience encored it; we played it again; it went even better the second time. On my return to the artists' room, I saw Habeneck standing with a slightly crestfallen air, and said casually as I went past, 'That's how it goes.' He did not reply.

In his *Life and Letters*, Sir Charles Hallé confirms that this was no vain exaggeration:

> Musicians who know the work, with its complicated rhythm, and all its intricacies, will easily understand how bold the venture was, and will wonder that it could be successful. But to see Berlioz during that performance was a sight never to be forgotten. He watched over every single member of the huge band; his beat was so decisive, his indication of all nuances so clear and so unmistakable, that the overture went smoothly, and no uninitiated person could guess at the absence of a rehearsal.

The overture was encored twice on its first performance in Vienna in the following year, though treated coolly in St. Petersburg in 1847 and hissed (thanks to an Italian cabal, Berlioz believed) when played as a prelude to Act 2 of the opera on 25 June 1853 during Berlioz's fourth visit to London.

[1] *The Memoirs of Hector Berlioz*, translated and edited by David Cairns. Gollancz, London 1969. Used here by permission.

However, in general the work was so enthusiastically received as to cause Berlioz's enemies some embarrassment.

The overture stands in somewhat similar relationship to its parent opera as Beethoven's *Leonore* overtures do to *Fidelio*; and it is, despite Berlioz's own acceptance of the practice, equally unsuitable for performance as an interlude. It is based on two themes from the opera. After a preliminary 'Carnival' flourish, the first theme heard is Cellini's aria to Teresa, 'O Teresa, vous que j'aime', from the Duo and Trio in Act 1 set in the house of her father the Papal Treasurer Balducci; to his sad declaration of love she replies, with equal sadness and to the same melody, that they must part. Originally in A flat (*Andante*), this becomes in the overture the C major cor anglais theme (*Andante sostenuto*) with Teresa's answer on violas in a sudden swerve to E major (bar 37); both statements of the melody are accompanied with figures similar to those used in the opera. The elaborate A major statement on full orchestra (bar 53), canonically with one version a single beat behind the other, already hints at the coming Carnival, during which Cellini and Teresa plan to elope; intricate percussion parts include tambourine and triangle. Thus prepared for the dance, the listener should not be surprised by the *poco animato* wind skirlings that precipitate the music into the *Allegro vivace* of the Carnival scene. In the opera, this saltarello was danced and sung *Presto scherzando* by the chorus in the Piazza Colonna in Scene 2 of Act 2; when he rewrote it in the overture, *Allegro vivace*, Berlioz originally notated it in 3/8, only later using the simpler and clearer 6/8 (a fact which may in part excuse Habeneck). He uses themes from this Roman Carnival scene, but works them symphonically with brilliant use of sudden leaps into unexpected keys and a fugato based on the love theme (bar 304).

Berlioz repeatedly emphasized the importance of speed in this section, once even interrupting an evidently lugubrious performance in Vienna for two pianos and physharmonica (an early form of harmonium) by shouting angrily, 'This is the carnival, not Lent. You make it sound like Good Friday in Rome.' One may add that he had himself experienced the real Roman Carnival during his stay in the city as a Prix de Rome winner in 1831. By long tradition, deriving from the ancient Saturnalia, it was the most hectic, licentious and violent of all Italy's pre-Lenten carnivals, and one which several Popes had unsuccessfully tried to restrain. Like Goethe, who witnessed it twice on his famous Italian journey, in 1787 and 1788, and found in it noise but no real merriment—'One has to see the Roman Carnival to lose all wish ever to see it again!'—Berlioz describes it brilliantly, but as his *Memoirs* show was in fact disgusted by what he too found an almost totally degrading spectacle.

The full score and parts of *Le Carnaval Romain* were published by Schlesinger in June 1844. The autograph seems to be lost apart from a single sheet in the Paris Conservatoire de Musique.

John Warrack, 1972

HECTOR BERLIOZ
Ouvertüre: *Römischer Karneval*, Op. 9

Obgleich Berlioz' *Benvenuto Cellini* bei der Erstaufführung in der Pariser Oper am 10. September 1838 nur Hohn geerntet hatte, blieb die Oper doch stets ein Lieblingswerk des Komponisten. Etwas über fünf Jahre später beschloss er, wenigstens einen Teil dieses Werks, das allem Anschein nach spurlos in der Versenkung verschwunden war, zu retten. Aus zwei Themen der Oper schuf er eine neue Konzertouvertüre, *ouverture caractéristique pour grand orchestre,* der er, nach dem zweiten der beiden Themen, den Titel *Carnaval Romain* gab. Die Ouvertüre wurde Fürst Friedrich von Hohenzollern-Hechingen, einem aufgeklärten Mäzen, der sich für die Musik von Berlioz einsetzte, gewidmet, bei dem der Komponist sich während einer Tournee in Deutschland 1842–3 aufgehalten hatte. Berlioz veranstaltete verschiedene Konzerte seiner Werke mit dem kleinen aber ausgezeichneten Orchester des Fürsten, der ihm nach dem letzten dieser Konzerte, im April, das Hohenzollernkreuz verlieh. Die erste Aufführung der Ouvertüre fand am 3. Februar 1844 unter der Leitung von Berlioz in dem Pariser Konzertsaal „Salle Herz" statt. Während der Proben für die Inszenierung der Oper, war er mit dem Dirigenten F.-A. Habeneck, der das von Berlioz verlangte schnelle Tempo des Saltarellos in der Karnevalszene nicht einhalten konnte, in Streit geraten. Als Habeneck erfuhr, dass Berlioz bei der Probe am Morgen der ersten Aufführung der Ouvertüre ohne seine Bläser, die dienstlich bei der Nationalgarde zu tun hatten, auskommen musste, kam er selbst zum Konzert, um zu beobachten, wie Berlioz sich aus der Affäre ziehen würde, zweifellos in der Hoffnung, einer den Erwartungen entsprechenden Katastrophe beiwohnen zu können. „Man kann ihn verstehen", bemerkte Berlioz in seinen *Memoiren:*

> In der Tat, als ich ins Orchester kam, bestürmten mich alle Bläser, empört darüber, dass sie eine Ouvertüre, die ihnen völlig unbekannt war, öffentlich aufführen sollten.
> „Kein Grund zur Sorge", sagte ich. „Die Stimmen sind fehlerfrei, und Sie sind alle ausgezeichnete Musiker. Behalten Sie meinen Stab so viel wie möglich im Auge, zählen Sie ihre Pausen genau, dann ist alles in Ordnung." Es wurde kein einziger Fehler gemacht. Ich begann das Allegro im richtigen Tempo, dem Wirbelwind-Tempo der römischen Tänzer. Das Publikum verlangte eine Wiederholung; wir spielten das Stück noch einmal; das zweite Mal ging es sogar noch besser. Als ich wieder ins Künstlerzimmer kam, sah ich Habeneck dort mit einer etwas beschämten Miene stehen. Im Vorbeigehen sagte ich beiläufig: „So muss das gehen." Er antwortete nicht.

Sir Charles Hallé bestätigt in seinem Buch *Life and Letters*, dass dies keine eitle Übertreibung war:

> Musiker, die das Werk mit seinen komplizierten Rhythmen und allen seinen Schwierigkeiten kennen, können leicht ermessen, wie kühn dieses Wagnis war, und sie werden sich fragen, wie es überhaupt erfolgreich sein konnte. Doch Berlioz bei dieser Aufführung zu beobachten, war ein unvergesslicher Anblick. Er passte auf jedes einzelne Mitglied dieses riesigen Orchesters auf; er taktierte mit einer solchen Entschiedenheit, und seine Angaben aller

Nuancen waren so klar und eindeutig, dass die Aufführung der Ouvertüre glatt vonstatten ging, und kein Uneingeweihter ahnen konnte, dass es ohne Probe geschah.

Die Ouvertüre musste bei ihrer ersten Aufführung in Wien im folgenden Jahr zweimal wiederholt werden, aber 1847, in St. Petersburg, war die Aufnahme kühl. In London wurde sie ausgezischt (dank einer italienischen Kabale, wie Berlioz glaubte), als sie am 25. Juni 1853, während Berlioz' viertem Aufenthalt in London, als Vorspiel zum zweiten Akt der Oper gespielt wurde. Im allgemeinen wurde das Werk jedoch so begeistert aufgenommen, dass Berlioz' Feinde dadurch in Verlegenheit gebracht wurden.

Die Ouvertüre verhält sich zu der Oper, der sie entstammt, ungefähr wie Beethovens *Leonore*-Ouvertüren zu Fidelio, und Berlioz' eigener Zustimmung zum Trotz, eignet sie sich ebenso wenig zur Zwischenaktmusik. Ihr thematisches Material beruht auf zwei Themen aus der Oper. Das erste Thema, das einem präludierenden „Karnevaltusch" folgt, ist Cellinis Arie an Teresa, „O Teresa, vous que j'aime", aus dem Duett und Terzett im Hause von Teresas Vater, dem päpstlichen Schatzmeister Balducci (erster Akt). Auf seine trauervolle Liebeserklärung antwortet sie mit derselben Melodie und der gleichen Traurigkeit und erklärt, dass sie scheiden müssen. Diese Passage, die ursprünglich in As-Dur (*Andante*) stand, wird in der Ouvertüre zum Thema des Englischhorns in C-Dur (*Andante sostenuto*). Die Bratschen übernehmen Teresas Antwort in einer plötzlichen Abweichung nach E-Dur (T. 37), und in beiden Fällen wird die Melodie von Figurationen begleitet, die den an dieser Stelle in der Oper verwandten ähnlich sind. Die reich ausgearbeitete Wiederholung des Themas für das ganze Orchester in A-Dur (T. 53) im Kanon, mit einem einzigen Taktschlag zwischen den beiden Einsätzen der Melodie, deutet schon durch seine komplizierten Schlagzeugstimmen, darunter Tamburin und Triangel, auf den bevorstehenden Karneval hin, den Cellini und Teresa dazu benutzen wollen, um zusammen zu entfliehen. Da hiermit die Stimmung für den Tanz vorbereitet wird, sollten die *poco animato* Bläserkapriolen, welche die Musik stark beschleunigen und zum Allegro vivace der Karnevalszene überleiten, den Hörer nicht überraschen. In der Oper wurde dieser Saltarello vom Chor auf der Piazza Colonna (zweiter Akt, zweite Szene) getanzt und gesungen (*Presto scherzando*). Als Berlioz den Tanz als *Allegro vivace* für die Ouvertüre umschrieb, gab er ursprünglich 3/8 an und setzte erst später dafür das einfachere und deutlichere Zeitmass 6/8 (was teilweise als Entschuldigung für Habeneck gelten mag). Er verwandte Themen aus seiner römischen Karnevalszene, doch führte er sie hier mit genialen, plötzlichen Sprüngen in unerwartete Tonarten, und einem, auf dem Liebesmotiv beruhenden Fugato (T. 304), symphonisch durch.

Wiederholt betonte Berlioz die Wichtigkeit eines schnellen Tempos in diesem Teil der Ouvertüre. Er unterbrach sogar einmal eine offensichtlich höchst traurige Aufführung eines Arrangements für zwei Klaviere und Physharmonica (eine frühe Form des Harmoniums) in Wien, indem er entrüstet ausrief: „Das soll Karneval, nicht Fastenzeit sein. So gespielt, klingt es wie ein Karfreitag in Rom." Es mag hinzugefügt werden, dass er den echten römischen Karneval selbst miterlebt hatte, während er sich 1831 in der Stadt, als Sieger im Wettbewerb um den Prix de Rome, aufhielt. Einer uralten Tradition folgend, die auf den Saturnalien der Antike beruht, war dieser Karneval der wildeste, zügelloseste und gewalttätigste aller italienischen Karnevale, die vor der Fastenzeit stattfanden. Verschiedene Päpste hatten vergeblich versucht, ihn in Schranken zu halten. Wie Goethe, der diesem Karneval zweimal auf seiner berühmtem Italienischen Reise 1787 und 1788 beigewohnt und nur Spektakel, aber keine echte Fröhlichkeit gefunden hatte —,,Das Carneval in Rom muss man gesehen haben, um den Wunsch völlig loszuwerden, es je wiederzusehen."—beschrieb Berlioz ihn glänzend, obwohl seine *Memoiren* beweisen, dass auch er von diesem fast völlig entwürdigenden Schauspiel in Wirklichkeit angewidert worden war.

Die Partitur und die Orchesterstimmen des *Carnaval Romain* wurden im Juni 1844 von Schlesinger herausgegeben. Das Autograph ist anscheinend, abgesehen von einem einzigen Blatt, das sich im Pariser Conservatoire de Musique befinden, abhanden gekommen.

John Warrack, 1972
Deutsche Übersetzung Stefan de Haan

HECTOR BERLIOZ
Ouverture: *Le Carnaval Romain*, Op. 9

Malgré la dérision du public pour *Benvenuto Cellini* lors de la première à l'Opéra de Paris le 10 septembre 1838, Berlioz garda toujours pour cette œuvre une certaine affection. Quelque cinq ans plus tard il décida d'en récupérer au moins une partie de l'oubli où elle avait sombré, et c'est à partir de deux motifs de l'opéra qu'il composa une nouvelle *Ouverture caractéristique pour grand orchestre* qu'il intitula, d'après le second de ces motifs, *Carnaval Romain*. Il la dédia au prince Friedrich von Hohenzollern, patron éclairé qui l'avait reçu chez lui lors de son voyage en Allemagne en 1842–43. Berlioz avait arrangé pour l'orchestre moins nombreux qu'excellent du prince plusieurs programmes de ses œuvres, dont le dernier lui avait valu la Croix de Hohenzollern.

L'ouverture fut exécutée pour la première fois à la Salle Herz à Paris, sous la direction du compositeur, le 3 février 1844. Or, il s'etait brouillé, lors des répétitions de l'opéra, avec le chef d'orchestre F.-A. Habeneck, incapable de parvenir à l'allure vive qu'il exigeait pour le saltarello de la scène du carnaval. En apprenant, donc, que le service de la Garde Nationale avait privé Berlioz de ses instruments à vent pour la répétition du jour même de la première, Habeneck se rendit au concert, curieux de voir comment Berlioz se tirerait de l'affaire et dans l'attente, sans doute, d'une catastrophe achevée. Et Berlioz raconte dans ses *Memoires :*

> «En arrivant à l'orchestre, en effet, tous les artistes chargés de la partie des instruments à vent m'entourèrent effrayés à l'idée de jouer devant le public une ouverture qui leur était entièrement inconnue.
>
> «-N'ayez pas peur, leur dis-je, les parties sont correctes, vous êtes tous des gens de talent, regardez mon bâton le plus souvent possible, comptez bien vos pauses et cela marchera.
>
> «Il n'y eut pas une seule faute. Je lançai l'allegro dans le mouvement tourbillonnant des danseurs transtéverins; le public cria *bis*; nous recommençâmes l'ouverture; elle fut encore mieux rendue la seconde fois; et en rentrant au foyer où se trouvait Habeneck un peu désappointé, je lui jetai en passant ces quatre mots: « Voilà ce que c'est!» auxquels il n'eut garde de répondre.»

Sir Charles Hallé confirme dans ses *Life and Letters* la justesse de ce rapport:

> «Les musiciens qui connaissent cette œuvre, avec son rythme complexe et ses multiples subtilités, comprendront tout de suite l'audace de cette initiative et s'étonneront de son succès. Mais la vue de Berlioz en cette occasion fut inoubliable. Il veilla sur chaque membre de l'immense orchestre; sa mesure fut si ferme, il signala chaque nuance d'une façon si claire que l'ouverture fut donnée sans méprise et personne ne se fût douté de la répétition manquée.»

L'ouverture reçut un accueil chaleureux à Vienne l'année suivante (le public réclama deux encores), froid à St-Petersbourg en 1847, et fut sifflée à Londres lorsqu'elle fut donnée comme prélude au second acte de l'opéra le 25 juin 1853 au cours du quatrième voyage de Berlioz à Londres. Il attribua cette mauvaise réception à une cabale italienne. En général, cependant, l'ouverture suscita un enthousiasme plutôt genant pour les ennemis du compositeur.

VIII

La relation de l'ouverture à l'opéra d'origine est à peu près celle des ouvertures *Léonore* de Beethoven à son *Fidelio* et la pratique, encore qu'acceptée de Berlioz, de la jouer comme entrelude est inadmissible pour l'une comme pour les autres.

Elle est bâtie sur deux motifs de l'opéra. Après une fanfare initiale de carnaval, on entend l'air que chante Cellini à Teresa, «O Teresa, vous que j'aime», tiré du Duo et Trio du premier acte qui se joue dans la maison de Balducci, trésorier du Pape et père de Teresa. A sa triste déclaralion d'amour elle répond, triste aussi, et sur la même mélodie, qu'ils doivent se quitter. A l'origine en la bémol (*Andante*), ce duo devient dans l'ouverture le motif pour cor anglais en ut majeur (*Andante sostenuto*) et la réponse de Teresa, sur altos, vire subitement en mi majeur (mesure 37). La mélodie est accompagnée chaque fois de figures semblables à celles de l'opéra. Un sujet majeur pour plein orchestre, joué en canon avec un écart d'une seule mesure, annonce déjà le carnaval qui s'approche et qui sera l'occasion de la fuite de Cellini et de Teresa, avec des parties complexes pour les instruments à percussion, y compris le tambourin et le triangle. La danse ainsi annoncée, les sons de pipeau *poco animato* qui précipitent la musique dans *l'Allegro vivace* du carnaval ne nous étonnent guère. Dans l'opéra c'était le chœur qui chantait et dansait ce saltarello, *Presto scherzando*, dans la Piazza Colonna, à la seconde scène du second acte; en le récrivant pour l'ouverture, Berlioz lui donna d'abord la mesure 3/8, qu'il ne simplifia que plus tard en 6/8 (ce qui peut nous donner une certaine indulgence pour Habeneck). Il emploie des motifs de la scène du carnaval romain, mais en les traitant symphoniquement, avec des sauts brillants en des tonalités inattendues et un fugato basé sur le motif des amoureux (mesure 304).

Berlioz souligna à maintes reprises l'importance de la vivacité dans cette section: lors d'une représentation lugubre à Vienne pour deux pianos et phisharmonica, il s'emporta et s'écria: «Mais ce n'est pas le carnaval, c'est le carême, c'est le vendredi saint de Rome que vous jouez là!» Il faut ajouter qu'il avait lui-même fait l'expérience du vrai carnaval romain lors de son séjour là-bas en tant que Prix de Rome en 1831. D'origine ancienne, dévolu des rites païens des Saturnales, c'était le plus frénétique, le plus lubrique et le plus violent de tous les carnavals pre-quadragésimaux de l'Italie. Comme Goethe, qui y avait assisté deux fois, en 1787 et 1788, lors de son célèbre voyage en Italie et qui n'y avait trouvé qu'un vacarme sans joie réelle—«Il faut voir le carnaval romain pour ne plus jamais désirer le revoir!»—Berlioz en donne une description brillante, mais en n'éprouvant, comme le montrent ses *Mémoires,* que du degoût devant ce spectacle avilissant.

La partition complète et les parties du *Carnaval Romain* furent données par Schlesinger en juin 1844. La partition autographe a disparu, à l'exception d'une seule feuille qui se trouve au Conservatoire de Paris.

John Warrack, 1972
Traduction française Genevieve Hawkins

Ouverture du Carnaval Romain

Allegro assai con fuoco   M.M. ♩.=156   Hector Berlioz, Op.9
1803-1869

N.º 620   E.E.8720

Ernst Eulenburg Ltd

2

E. E. 3720

6

E. E. 3720

10

E. E. 3720

14

E. E. 3720

17

E. E. 3720

18

E. E. 3720

E. E. 3720

24

170

E. E. 3720

180

E. E. 3720

32

E. E. 3720

36

E. E. 3720

42

E. E. 3720

44

46

E. E 3720

56

58

E. E. 3720